Character
Companion

for the Miller Family Series

A Godly Character Bible Study

Kristyn A. Hage

THIS BOOK BELONGS TO

Illustrated by

Lana Martin

Character Companion

for the Miller Family Series

Kristyn A. Hage

But ask now the beasts, and they shall teach thee; and the fowls of the air, and they shall tell thee:

Or speak to the earth, and it shall teach thee: and the fishes of the sea shall declare unto thee.

Who knoweth not in all these that the hand of the LORD hath wrought this?

Job 12:7-9

Character Companion
2nd Edition
Copyright GPP 2013   All Rights Reserved
Mildred A. Martin, General editor
Word definitions by GPP staff and
Webster's 1828 Dictionary
Printing & binding by:
C-M Books   4- 2015

Green Pastures Press

50 Green Pastures Lane, Mifflin, PA 17058

Printed in USA
ISBN 9781-884377-24-2

Introduction and Instructions

The *Character Companion* is a complementary workbook for the *Miller Family Series,* designed to help children from preschool on up to apply the truth of God's Word to their daily lives. This book contains 50 character qualities that are taught in Scripture and reinforced by the Miller family stories. You can make this workbook adaptable to various ages by using some or all of the following activities:

1. Color the picture.

2. Explain how the picture portrays the character quality, either verbally or on the lines provided.

3. Read the Scripture verses and arrange them in order as they would appear in the Bible. Use one or more of the suggested stories to accompany each lesson.

4. List synonyms and antonyms. See how many you can think of first, and then check a thesaurus.

5. Give the noun form for each adjective. (See page 60 for answer key)

6. From the Scripture passages given, find a Bible character who exemplifies each quality and tell or write how this person displayed the character quality. Example: Meek - Moses, Xenophilic - Martha

7. Pages 54-59 provide matching exercises to reinforce the character meanings.

Focusing on one character quality for about a week gives opportunity to enjoy the suggested Miller stories and apply the Scriptures studied.

"Let the word of Christ dwell in you richly with all wisdom..." Colossians 3:16

This Bible study is to be used as a complement to the Miller Family Series,

by Mildred A. Martin, published by Green Pastures Press:

Storytime with the Millers

Wisdom and the Millers

Missionary Stories with the Millers

Prudence and the Millers

School Days with the Millers

Growing with the Millers

ALERT

Quick to detect; watchful; wide awake; guarding against surprise or danger

Can you explain how this picture describes the character quality?

_____

_____

_____

_____

Scripture: 1 Peter 5:8; Matthew 24:42-44; 1 Samuel 18:10-11; Ephesians 5:15, 6:18

_____

Stories: School Days Ch. 23; Wisdom Ch. 16; Prudence Ch. 9; Growing Ch. 22

Synonyms: _____

Antonyms: _____

Noun form of Alert: _____

What person in the Bible illustrates this quality? Tell how: _____

_____

_____

Application: Write or draw how you can show this character trait.

Quick to detect; watchful; wide awake; guarding against surprise or danger

ATTENTIVE

To listen or look at with interest; to pay attention; to closely follow; regarding with care

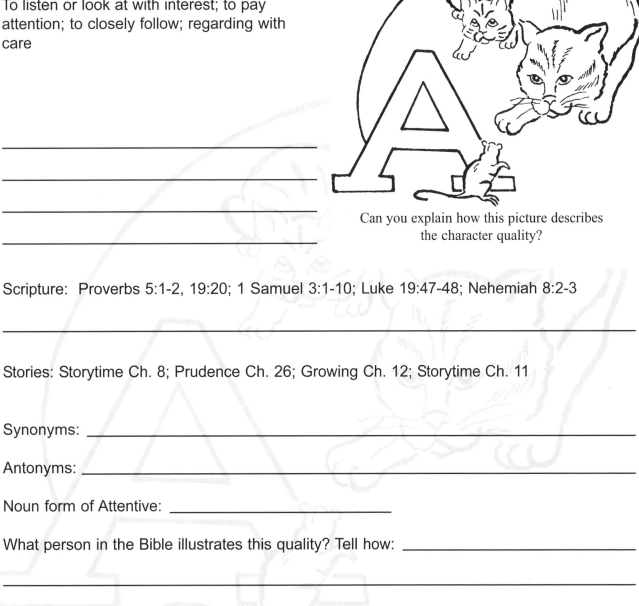

Can you explain how this picture describes the character quality?

_____
_____
_____
_____

Scripture: Proverbs 5:1-2, 19:20; 1 Samuel 3:1-10; Luke 19:47-48; Nehemiah 8:2-3

_____

Stories: Storytime Ch. 8; Prudence Ch. 26; Growing Ch. 12; Storytime Ch. 11

Synonyms: _____

Antonyms: _____

Noun form of Attentive: _____

What person in the Bible illustrates this quality? Tell how: _____

_____
_____

Application: Write or draw how you can show this character trait.

BRAVE

Courageous; fearless; doing what is right in spite of danger or hardships

_____

_____

_____

_____

Can you explain how this picture describes the character quality?

Scripture: Psalm 27:1-3; Joshua 1:6-9; 2 Timothy 1:7; Deuteronomy 31:6-8

_____

Stories: Missionary Stories Ch. 3 & 4; Growing Ch. 2 & 8

Synonyms: _____

Antonyms: _____

Noun form of Brave: _____

What person in the Bible illustrates this quality? Tell how: _____

_____

_____

Application: Write or draw how you can show this character trait.

Courageous; fearless; doing what is right in spite of danger or hardships

CONFIDENT

Sure of; without doubt or hesitancy; having full belief; trusting

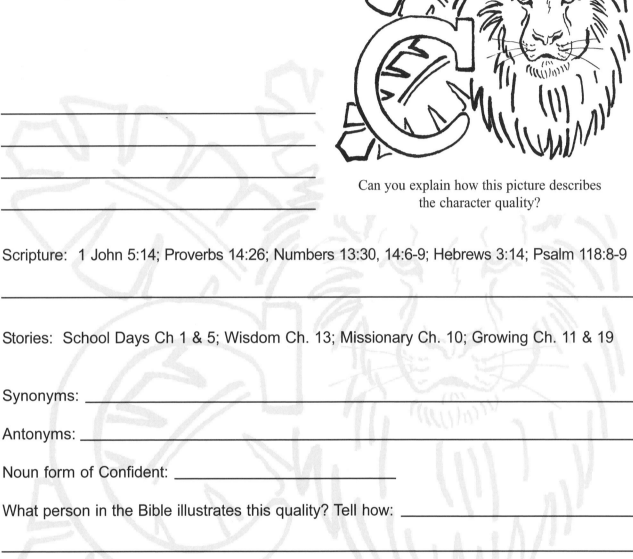

Can you explain how this picture describes the character quality?

_____
_____
_____
_____

Scripture: 1 John 5:14; Proverbs 14:26; Numbers 13:30, 14:6-9; Hebrews 3:14; Psalm 118:8-9

_____

Stories: School Days Ch 1 & 5; Wisdom Ch. 13; Missionary Ch. 10; Growing Ch. 11 & 19

Synonyms: _____

Antonyms: _____

Noun form of Confident: _____

What person in the Bible illustrates this quality? Tell how: _____
_____
_____

Application: Write or draw how you can show this character trait.

CONTENT

Satisfied; happily restful or peaceful; not covetous or greedy; having a mind at peace

Can you explain how this picture describes the character quality?

_____

_____

_____

_____

Scripture: 2 Corinthians 12:7-10; Hebrews 13:5; 1 Timothy 6:6-8; Philippians 4:11-13

_____

Stories: School Days Ch. 3 & 16; Wisdom Ch. 15; Growing Ch. 17

Synonyms: _____

Antonyms: _____

Noun form of Content: _____

What person in the Bible illustrates this quality? Tell how: _____

_____

_____

Application: Write or draw how you can show this character trait.

Satisfied; happily restful or peaceful; not covetous or greedy; having a mind at peace

DILIGENT

Careful; putting forth earnest and honest effort; not lazy or slothful; constant in effort to accomplish what is undertaken

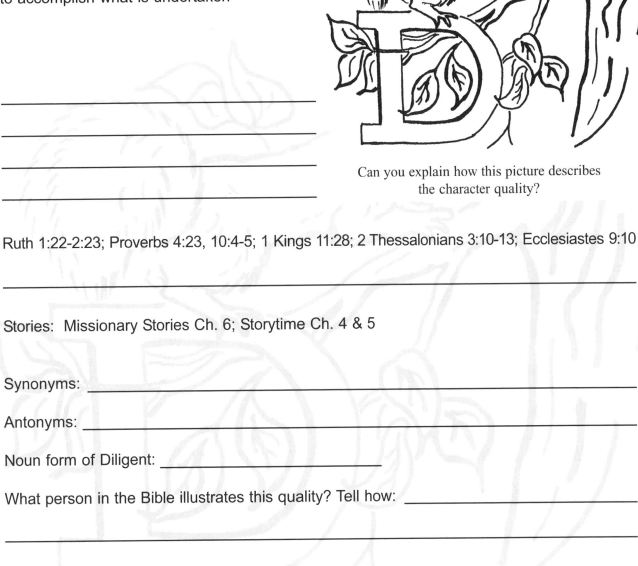

Can you explain how this picture describes the character quality?

_____

_____

_____

_____

Ruth 1:22-2:23; Proverbs 4:23, 10:4-5; 1 Kings 11:28; 2 Thessalonians 3:10-13; Ecclesiastes 9:10

_____

Stories: Missionary Stories Ch. 6; Storytime Ch. 4 & 5

Synonyms: _____

Antonyms: _____

Noun form of Diligent: _____

What person in the Bible illustrates this quality? Tell how: _____

_____

_____

Application: Write or draw how you can show this character trait.

Careful; putting forth earnest and honest effort; not lazy or slothful; constant in effort to accomplish what is undertaken

9

DISCERNING

Insightful; ability to accurately determine right from wrong; having keen understanding

_____

_____

_____

_____

Can you explain how this picture describes the character quality?

Scripture: Proverbs 2:1-13; Hebrews 5:12-14; Joshua 9; Ecclesiastes 8:5

_____

Stories: Wisdom Ch. 19 & 20; Growing Ch. 15

Synonyms: _____

Antonyms: _____

Noun form of Discerning: _____

What person in the Bible illustrates this quality? Tell how: _____

_____

_____

Application: Write or draw how you can show this character trait.

Insightful; ability to accurately determine right from wrong; having keen understanding

DISCIPLINED

Able to control oneself; well behaved and self-motivated; subjected to rules and regulations

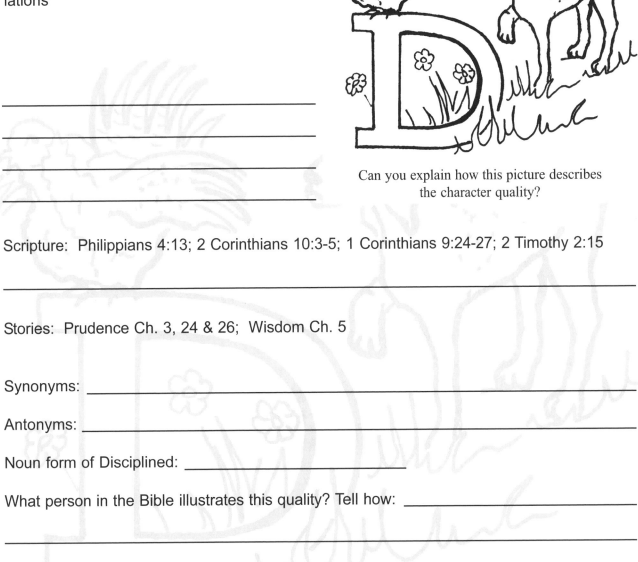

Can you explain how this picture describes the character quality?

_____

_____

_____

Scripture: Philippians 4:13; 2 Corinthians 10:3-5; 1 Corinthians 9:24-27; 2 Timothy 2:15

_____

Stories: Prudence Ch. 3, 24 & 26; Wisdom Ch. 5

Synonyms: _____

Antonyms: _____

Noun form of Disciplined: _____

What person in the Bible illustrates this quality? Tell how: _____

_____

_____

Application: Write or draw how you can show this character trait.

ENCOURAGING

Giving good advice or council that is beneficial, uplifting or edifying; words or deeds that give courage to another; inspiring with hope and confidence

_____
_____
_____
_____

Can you explain how this picture describes the character quality?

Scripture: Proverbs 12:25; Hebrews 3:12-13, 10:24-25; 1 Samuel 30:6; Acts 11:22-26

_____

Stories: Prudence Ch. 25; School Days Ch. 15 & 19; Growing Ch. 4; Missionary Ch. 19

Synonyms: _____

Antonyms: _____

Noun form of Encouraging: _____

What person in the Bible illustrates this quality? Tell how: _____
_____
_____

Application: Write or draw how you can show this character trait.

Giving good advice or council that is beneficial, uplifting or edifying; words or deeds that give courage to another; inspiring with hope and confidence

FAITHFUL

Reliable; dependable; obedient; standing firm to a belief or practice; firmly adhering to duty; loyal

_____

_____

_____

Can you explain how this picture describes the character quality?

Scripture: Daniel 6:1-10; Luke 16:10-13; Hebrews 11:6-7; Matthew 25:14-28

_____

Stories: Missionary Stories Ch. 9; School Days Ch. 2; Storytime Ch. 5; Growing Ch. 8

Synonyms: _____

Antonyms: _____

Noun form of Faithful: _____

What person in the Bible illustrates this quality? Tell how: _____

_____

_____

Application: Write or draw how you can show this character trait.

Reliable; dependable; obedient; standing firm to a belief or practice; firmly adhering to duty; loyal

FORGIVING

Giving up personal revenge, spite or ill will against a person that has wronged you; not holding a grudge against; pardoning

Can you explain how this picture describes the character quality?

_____

_____

_____

_____

Scripture: Colossians 3:12-13; Romans 12:19-21; Matthew 6:14-15, 18:21-35

_____

Stories: School Days Ch. 7, 10 & 13; Growing Ch. 15

Synonyms: _____

Antonyms: _____

Noun form of Forgiving: _____

What person in the Bible illustrates this quality? Tell how: _____

_____

_____

Application: Write or draw how you can show this character trait.

Giving up personal revenge, spite or ill will against a person that has wronged you; not holding a grudge against; pardoning

FRIENDLY

Socially kind and agreeable; expressing a feeling of openness and love towards another

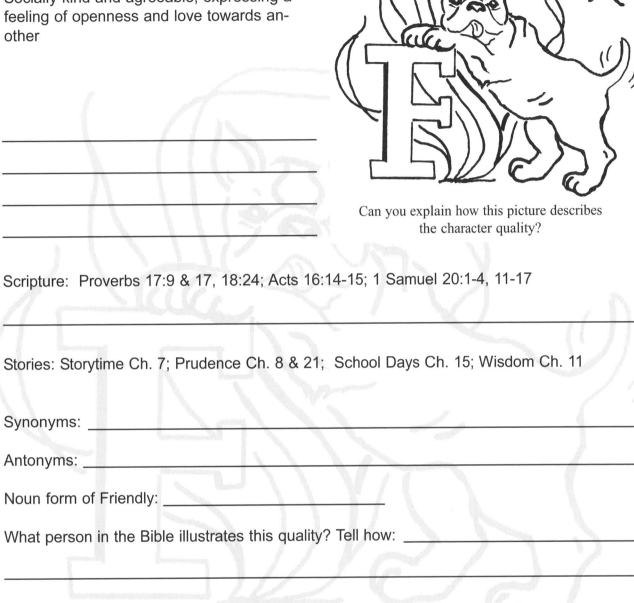

Can you explain how this picture describes the character quality?

_____

_____

_____

_____

Scripture: Proverbs 17:9 & 17, 18:24; Acts 16:14-15; 1 Samuel 20:1-4, 11-17

_____

Stories: Storytime Ch. 7; Prudence Ch. 8 & 21; School Days Ch. 15; Wisdom Ch. 11

Synonyms: _____

Antonyms: _____

Noun form of Friendly: _____

What person in the Bible illustrates this quality? Tell how: _____

_____

_____

Application: Write or draw how you can show this character trait.

GENEROUS

Granting or giving plenty; willingness to give ample or liberal amount

Can you explain how this picture describes the character quality?

_____

_____

_____

_____

Scripture: John 6:5-14; Matthew 6:19-21; 2 Corinthians 9:6-7; Luke 6:35-38, 19:1-10

_____

Stories: Wisdom Ch. 8; Missionary Stories (Introduction); Growing Ch. 6; Missionary Ch. 12

Synonyms: _____

Antonyms: _____

Noun form of Generous: _____

What person in the Bible illustrates this quality? Tell how: _____

_____

_____

Application: Write or draw how you can show this character trait.

Granting or giving plenty; willingness to give ample or liberal amount

GENTLE

Patient and kind help or disposition; mild and peaceable behavior; soothing, not harsh

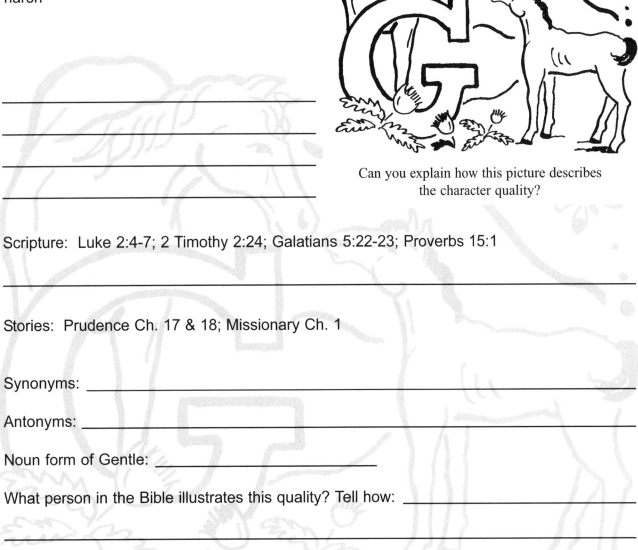

Can you explain how this picture describes the character quality?

_____

_____

_____

Scripture: Luke 2:4-7; 2 Timothy 2:24; Galatians 5:22-23; Proverbs 15:1

_____

Stories: Prudence Ch. 17 & 18; Missionary Ch. 1

Synonyms: _____

Antonyms: _____

Noun form of Gentle: _____

What person in the Bible illustrates this quality? Tell how: _____

_____

_____

Application: Write or draw how you can show this character trait.

GODLY

Like or similar to God; righteous; living in obedience to God's commands, out of love for Him and reverence for His character and precepts

Can you explain how this picture describes
the character quality?

_____

_____

_____

_____

Scripture: 2 Peter 1:5-8; 1 Timothy 4:7-8, 6:6-11; Acts 13:21-22

_____

Stories: School Days Ch. 14 & 17; Wisdom Ch. 25; Growing Ch. 13; Missionary Ch. 5

Synonyms: _____

Antonyms: _____

Noun form of Godly: _____

What person in the Bible illustrates this quality? Tell how: _____

_____

_____

Application: Write or draw how you can show this character trait.

*Like or similar to God; righteous; living in obedience to God's
commands, out of love for Him and reverence for His character and precepts*

GOOD

That which is right, sound and beneficial; without significant fault or defect; virtuous; proper; favorable to happiness

Can you explain how this picture describes the character quality?

_____
_____
_____
_____

Scripture: Acts 9:36-41; Matthew 5:16; Ephesians 2:8-10; Genesis 6:8-9; Galatians 5:22-23

_____

Stories: School Days 7 & 12; Prudence Ch. 4

Synonyms: _____

Antonyms: _____

Noun form of Good: _____

What person in the Bible illustrates this quality? Tell how: _____

_____
_____

Application: Write or draw how you can show this character trait.

That which is right, sound and beneficial; without significant fault or defect; virtuous; proper; favorable to happiness

19

HELPFUL

Ready to be of service or assistance; useful; willing to help

Can you explain how this picture describes the character quality?

_____

_____

_____

_____

Scripture: Genesis 2:18-22; Hebrews 13:5-6; 2 Kings 5:1-4; Acts 16:9-10

_____

Stories: Missionary Stories Ch. 22; Storytime Ch. 3; Wisdom Ch. 6; Growing Ch. 21

Synonyms: _____

Antonyms: _____

Noun form of Helpful: _____

What person in the Bible illustrates this quality? Tell how: _____

_____

_____

Application: Write or draw how you can show this character trait.

Ready to be of service or assistance; useful; willing to help

HOLY

Without sin or fault, pure, undefiled, righteous, perfect; (God is holy in the absolute sense of the word. Man can be a partaker of God's holiness.)

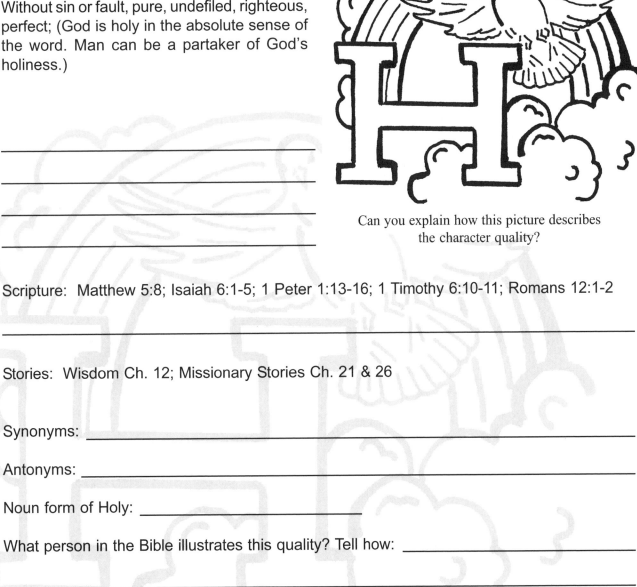

Can you explain how this picture describes the character quality?

_____

_____

_____

Scripture: Matthew 5:8; Isaiah 6:1-5; 1 Peter 1:13-16; 1 Timothy 6:10-11; Romans 12:1-2

_____

Stories: Wisdom Ch. 12; Missionary Stories Ch. 21 & 26

Synonyms: _____

Antonyms: _____

Noun form of Holy: _____

What person in the Bible illustrates this quality? Tell how: _____

_____

_____

Application: Write or draw how you can show this character trait.

Without sin or fault, pure, undefiled, righteous, perfect; (God is holy in the absolute sense of the word. Man can be a partaker of God's holiness.)

21

HONEST

Can you explain how this picture describes the character quality?

Truthful; standing by the right even under pressure; giving fair value or measure; not cheating

_____

_____

_____

_____

Scripture: 1 Thessalonians 4:11-12; John 1:45-50; Proverbs 11:1; Romans 12:17

_____

Stories: Storytime Ch. 12; Wisdom Ch. 23; School Days Ch. 7 & 21; Growing Ch. 18

Synonyms: _____

Antonyms: _____

Noun form of Honest: _____

What person in the Bible illustrates this quality? Tell how: _____

_____

_____

Application: Write or draw how you can show this character trait.

Truthful; standing by the right even under pressure; giving fair value or measure; not cheating

HUMBLE

A quality of heart that is meek, quiet and gentle; not boastful, proud or showing off; not demanding

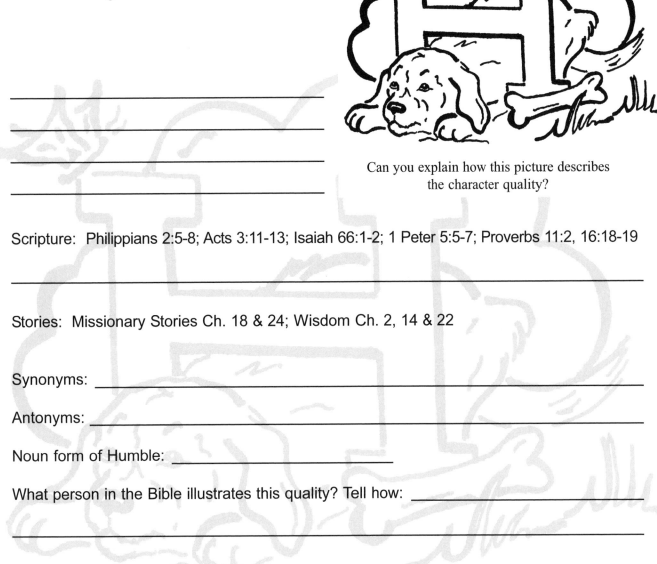

Can you explain how this picture describes the character quality?

_____

_____

_____

_____

Scripture: Philippians 2:5-8; Acts 3:11-13; Isaiah 66:1-2; 1 Peter 5:5-7; Proverbs 11:2, 16:18-19

_____

Stories: Missionary Stories Ch. 18 & 24; Wisdom Ch. 2, 14 & 22

Synonyms: _____

Antonyms: _____

Noun form of Humble: _____

What person in the Bible illustrates this quality? Tell how: _____

_____

_____

Application: Write or draw how you can show this character trait.

INNOCENT

Without guilt or shame; free of wrong; blameless; pure

_____

_____

_____

_____

Can you explain how this picture describes the character quality?

Scripture: 1 John 2:15-17; Daniel 6:3-4, 21-22; Matthew 10:16; Psalm 19:13,14; 2 Timothy 2:22

_____

Stories: Prudence Ch. 16; Storytime Ch. 10; Growing Ch. 14

Synonyms: _____

Antonyms: _____

Noun form of Innocent: _____

What person in the Bible illustrates this quality? Tell how: _____

_____

_____

Application: Write or draw how you can show this character trait.

Without guilt or shame; free of wrong; blameless; pure

JOYFUL

Full of joy; happy and thankful

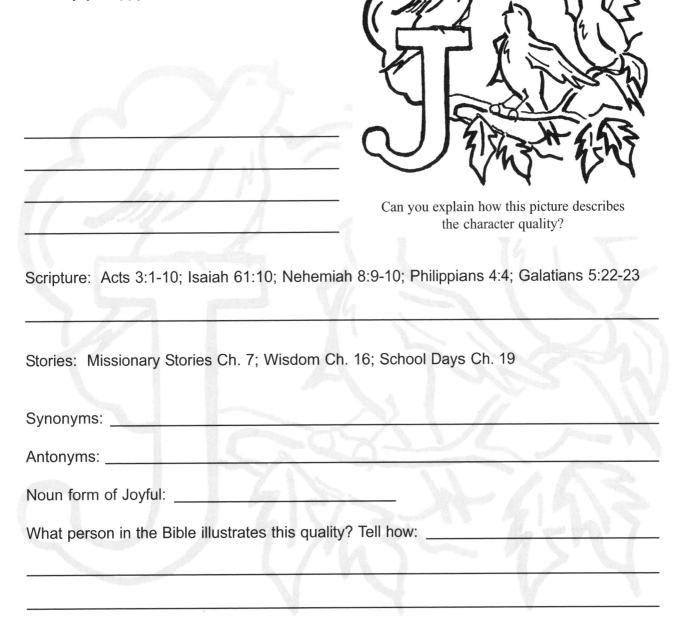

Can you explain how this picture describes
the character quality?

_____

_____

_____

_____

Scripture: Acts 3:1-10; Isaiah 61:10; Nehemiah 8:9-10; Philippians 4:4; Galatians 5:22-23

Stories: Missionary Stories Ch. 7; Wisdom Ch. 16; School Days Ch. 19

Synonyms: _____

Antonyms: _____

Noun form of Joyful: _____

What person in the Bible illustrates this quality? Tell how: _____

_____

_____

Application: Write or draw how you can show this character trait.

KIND

Considerate and gracious; helpful; agreeable or benevolent in attitude and actions; looking out for the welfare of others often at the expense of self-comfort

Can you explain how this picture describes the character quality?

_____

_____

_____

_____

Scripture: Ephesians 4:32; 2 Samuel 9:1-7; Luke 6:35; Proverbs 31:26

_____

Stories: School Days Ch. 8 & 15; Wisdom Ch. 7 & 8; Growing Ch. 1

Synonyms: _____

Antonyms: _____

Noun form of Kind: _____

What person in the Bible illustrates this quality? Tell how: _____

_____

_____

Application: Write or draw how you can show this character trait.

Considerate and gracious; helpful; agreeable or benevolent in attitude and actions; looking out for the welfare of others often at the expense of self-comfort

KNOWLEDGEABLE

Possessing and understanding a wide range of truth and facts; well informed

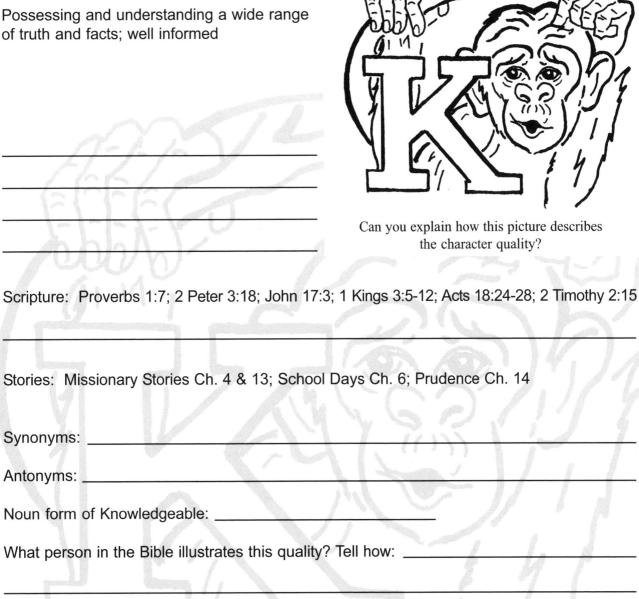

Can you explain how this picture describes the character quality?

_____
_____
_____
_____

Scripture: Proverbs 1:7; 2 Peter 3:18; John 17:3; 1 Kings 3:5-12; Acts 18:24-28; 2 Timothy 2:15

_____

Stories: Missionary Stories Ch. 4 & 13; School Days Ch. 6; Prudence Ch. 14

Synonyms: _____

Antonyms: _____

Noun form of Knowledgeable: _____

What person in the Bible illustrates this quality? Tell how: _____

_____
_____

Application: Write or draw how you can show this character trait.

LOVING

To be devoted to, kindly care for, admiring of; genuine love includes the qualities of self-sacrificing and commitment to another

Can you explain how this picture describes the character quality?

_____

_____

_____

_____

Scripture: Colossians 3:14; Galatians 5:22-23; 1 John 4:7-11; John 3:16-17, 13:34-35, 21:13-17

_____

Stories: School Days Ch. 4; Wisdom Ch. 18; Missionary Stories Ch. 27

Synonyms: _____

Antonyms: _____

Noun form of Loving: _____

What person in the Bible illustrates this quality? Tell how: _____

_____

_____

Application: Write or draw how you can show this character trait.

To be devoted to, kindly care for, admiring of; genuine love includes the qualities of self-sacrificing and commitment to another

MEEK

Lowly in heart, humble, not boastful or proud; wanting to quietly do the right thing; submissive obedience; given to forbearance under injuries

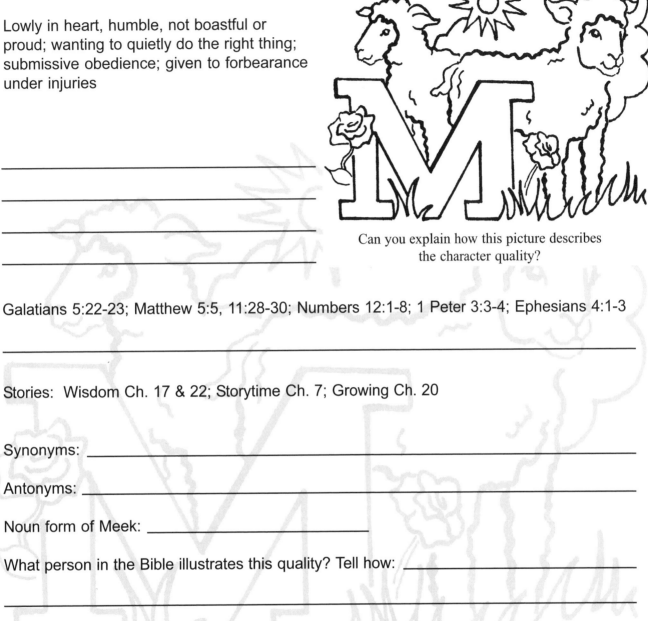

Can you explain how this picture describes the character quality?

_____
_____
_____
_____

Galatians 5:22-23; Matthew 5:5, 11:28-30; Numbers 12:1-8; 1 Peter 3:3-4; Ephesians 4:1-3

_____

Stories: Wisdom Ch. 17 & 22; Storytime Ch. 7; Growing Ch. 20

Synonyms: _____

Antonyms: _____

Noun form of Meek: _____

What person in the Bible illustrates this quality? Tell how: _____
_____
_____

Application: Write or draw how you can show this character trait.

Lowly in heart, humble, not boastful or proud; wanting to quietly do the right thing; submissive obedience; given to forbearance under injuries

29

MERCIFUL

Graciously forbearing and forgiving; kindly withholding punishment due to an offender; compassionate

Can you explain how this picture describes the character quality?

_____
_____
_____
_____

Scripture: Luke 6:35-36, 15:11-24; Matthew 5:7; 1 Peter 3:8-9; Titus 3:4-6

_____

Stories: Missionary Stories Ch. 16 & 17; School Days Ch. 4; Storytime Ch. 1

Synonyms: _____

Antonyms: _____

Noun form of Merciful: _____

What person in the Bible illustrates this quality? Tell how: _____

_____

_____

Application: Write or draw how you can show this character trait.

Graciously forbearing and forgiving; kindly withholding punishment due to an offender; compassionate

NEAT

Orderly; tidy; harmonious arrangement; well kept

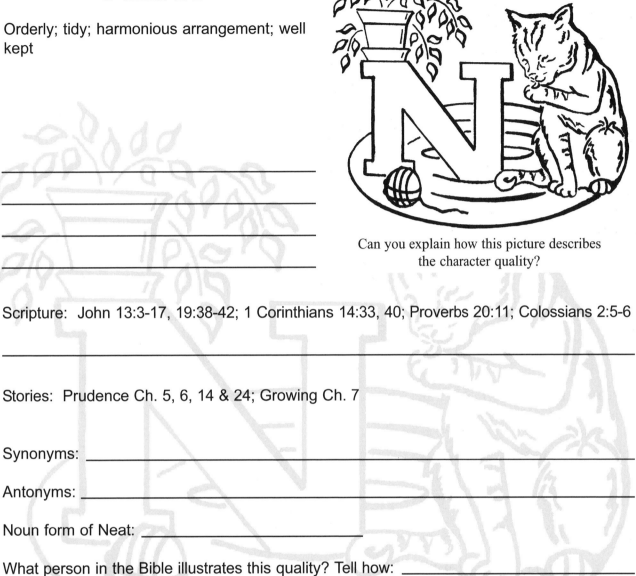

Can you explain how this picture describes the character quality?

_____

_____

_____

Scripture: John 13:3-17, 19:38-42; 1 Corinthians 14:33, 40; Proverbs 20:11; Colossians 2:5-6

_____

Stories: Prudence Ch. 5, 6, 14 & 24; Growing Ch. 7

Synonyms: _____

Antonyms: _____

Noun form of Neat: _____

What person in the Bible illustrates this quality? Tell how: _____

_____

_____

Application: Write or draw how you can show this character trait.

OBEDIENT

Can you explain how this picture describes
the character quality?

Following directions or commands; doing
what one is supposed to do or not doing
what is not allowed; submission to authority

_____

_____

_____

_____

Scripture: Colossians 3:20; John 14:15, 23; Acts 5:26-32; 1 Samuel 15:12-25; Daniel 3:8-18

_____

Stories: Storytime Ch. 2; School Days Ch. 18 & 20; Growing Ch. 7 & 14

Synonyms: _____

Antonyms: _____

Noun form of Obedient: _____

What person in the Bible illustrates this quality? Tell how: _____

_____

_____

Application: Write or draw how you can show this character trait.

*Following directions or commands;
doing what one is supposed to do or not doing what is not allowed; submission to authority*

PATIENT

Quietly waiting; not frustrated or hurried; contentedly waiting on God's timing; not overly demanding of others; not easily upset

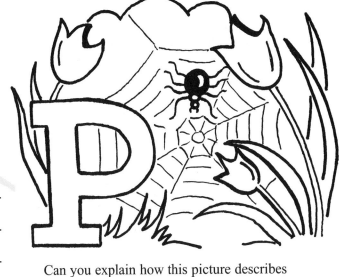

Can you explain how this picture describes the character quality?

_____

_____

_____

_____

Scripture: Colossians 1:9-12; 1 Peter 2:19-21; Job 1:13-22; James 1:2-4, 5:11; Galatians 5:22-23

_____

Stories: Missionary Stories Ch. 3 & 6; Growing Ch. 9

Synonyms: _____

Antonyms: _____

Noun form of Patient: _____

What person in the Bible illustrates this quality? Tell how: _____

_____

_____

Application: Write or draw how you can show this character trait.

Quietly waiting; not frustrated or hurried; contentedly waiting on God's timing; not overly demanding of others; not easily upset

PEACEABLE

Able to make relationships happy and har-monious; bringing unity; not causing strife or ill feelings; quiet and restful

_____

_____

_____

_____

Can you explain how this picture describes the character quality?

Scripture: Matthew 5:9; Genesis 26:17-25; James 3:17-18; Romans 12:18

_____

Stories: Wisdom Ch. 14; School Days Ch. 10 & 15; Growing Ch. 3

Synonyms: _____

Antonyms: _____

Noun form of Peaceable: _____

What person in the Bible illustrates this quality? Tell how: _____

_____

_____

Application: Write or draw how you can show this character trait.

Able to make relationships happy and harmonious; bringing unity; not causing strife or ill feelings; quiet and restful

PERSEVERING

Continuing on even though there are difficult obstacles; faithful; not giving up or turning back

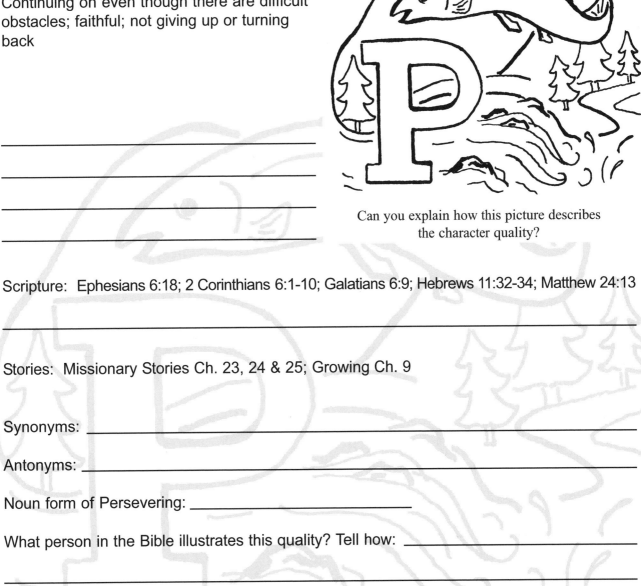

Can you explain how this picture describes the character quality?

_____

_____

_____

_____

Scripture: Ephesians 6:18; 2 Corinthians 6:1-10; Galatians 6:9; Hebrews 11:32-34; Matthew 24:13

_____

Stories: Missionary Stories Ch. 23, 24 & 25; Growing Ch. 9

Synonyms: _____

Antonyms: _____

Noun form of Persevering: _____

What person in the Bible illustrates this quality? Tell how: _____

_____

_____

Application: Write or draw how you can show this character trait.

PRUDENT

Insightful; good at avoiding danger or trouble; good judgment; cautious; circumspect; wise

Can you explain how this picture describes the character quality?

_____

_____

_____

_____

Scripture: Proverbs 8:12-13, 14:15-16, 15:5, 16:20-21, 22:3-4; 1 Samuel 25:14-35

_____

Stories: Prudence Ch. 1 & 12; School Days Ch. 9; Wisdom Ch. 1 & 21

Synonyms: _____

Antonyms: _____

Noun form of Prudent: _____

What person in the Bible illustrates this quality? Tell how: _____

_____

_____

Application: Write or draw how you can show this character trait.

Insightful; good at avoiding danger or trouble; good judgment; cautious; circumspect; wise

QUIET

Restful silence; absence of noise or commotion; still, peaceful

_____

_____

_____

_____

Can you explain how this picture describes
the character quality?

Scripture: Isaiah 30:15; 1 Timothy 2:1-4; Psalm 23; 1 Samuel 26; 1 Thessalonians 4:11-12

_____

Stories: Storytime Ch. 8; Prudence Ch. 2 & 26

Synonyms: _____

Antonyms: _____

Noun form of Quiet: _____

What person in the Bible illustrates this quality? Tell how: _____

_____

_____

Application: Write or draw how you can show this character trait.

Restful silence; absence of noise or commotion; still, peaceful

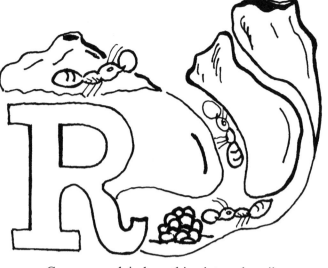

RESOURCEFUL

Thrifty; good at making do with what you have at hand; creative

_____

_____

_____

_____

Can you explain how this picture describes
the character quality?

Scripture: Matthew 25:14-29; Philippians 4:19; 2 Corinthians 9:8; Exodus 2:1-10

_____

Stories: Missionary Stories Ch. 9 & Conclusion; Storytime Ch. 1 & 9

Synonyms: _____

Antonyms: _____

Noun form of Resourceful: _____

What person in the Bible illustrates this quality? Tell how: _____

_____

_____

Application: Write or draw how you can show this character trait.

Thrifty; good at making do with what you have at hand; creative

RESPECTFUL

Showing proper behavior and response toward others; treating others with dignity or kindness and esteem; using things in a careful way

_____

_____

_____

_____

Can you explain how this picture describes the character quality?

Scripture: Daniel 6:19-23; 1 Thessalonians 5:12-13; Psalm 119:117; Philippians 2:3-4

_____

Stories: Prudence Ch. 21 & 27; Storytime Ch. 8; Growing Ch. 16

Synonyms: _____

Antonyms: _____

Noun form of Respectful: _____

What person in the Bible illustrates this quality? Tell how: _____

_____

_____

Application: Write or draw how you can show this character trait.

Showing proper behavior and response toward others; treating others with dignity or kindness and esteem; using things in a careful way

39

RESPONSIBLE

Reliable; trustworthy; fulfilling one's duties promptly and carefully; accountable

_____

_____

_____

_____

Can you explain how this picture describes the character quality?

Scripture: 1 Thessalonians 4:11-12; Genesis 41:46-49, 53-57; Colossians 1:9-10; Exodus 40:16

_____

Stories: Storytime Ch. 5; Wisdom Ch. 9; Prudence Ch. 10

Synonyms: _____

Antonyms: _____

Noun form of Responsible: _____

What person in the Bible illustrates this quality? Tell how: _____

_____

_____

Application: Write or draw how you can show this character trait.

Reliable; trustworthy; fulfilling one's duties promptly and carefully; accountable

SELF-CONTROLLED

Able to keep one's appetites, desires and emotions in proper balance to what is wholesome and expedient; temperate; self-restraint

_____

_____

_____

_____

Can you explain how this picture describes the character quality?

Scripture: 2 Peter 1:5-10; 1 Corinthians 9:24-27; Genesis 43:16, 24-34; Galatians 5:22-23

_____

Stories: Prudence Ch. 13; Storytime Ch 6; Wisdom Ch. 17

Synonyms: _____

Antonyms: _____

Noun form of Self-Controlled: _____

What person in the Bible illustrates this quality? Tell how: _____

_____

Application: Write or draw how you can show this character trait.

SERVING

Helping others, often at the expense of one's own interests; sensing what should be done by way of duty or need and doing it

Can you explain how this picture describes the character quality?

_____
_____
_____
_____

Scripture: Colossians 3:23-24; John 12:1-3, 13:3-17; Galatians 5:13; Luke 10:38-42

_____

Stories: Missionary Stories Ch. 13, 22 & 24; School Days Ch. 22

Synonyms: _____

Antonyms: _____

Noun form of Serving: _____

What person in the Bible illustrates this quality? Tell how: _____

_____

_____

Application: Write or draw how you can show this character trait.

SUBMISSIVE

Willing obedience; yielding one's will to the will of another; a humble person will have a submissive attitude

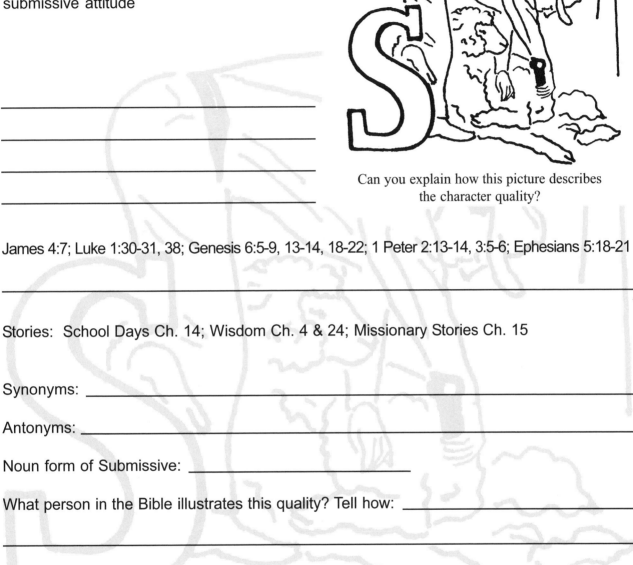

Can you explain how this picture describes the character quality?

_____

_____

_____

_____

James 4:7; Luke 1:30-31, 38; Genesis 6:5-9, 13-14, 18-22; 1 Peter 2:13-14, 3:5-6; Ephesians 5:18-21

_____

Stories: School Days Ch. 14; Wisdom Ch. 4 & 24; Missionary Stories Ch. 15

Synonyms: _____

Antonyms: _____

Noun form of Submissive: _____

What person in the Bible illustrates this quality? Tell how: _____

_____

_____

Application: Write or draw how you can show this character trait.

THANKFUL

Having a feeling or attitude of appreciation; grateful; expressing gratitude for a benefit received from another

Can you explain how this picture describes the character quality?

_____

_____

_____

_____

Scripture: Ephesians 5:20; Philippians 4:6; Daniel 6:10; 1 Thessalonians 5:18; Luke 17:11-19

_____

Stories: Missionary Stories Ch. 28; Prudence Ch. 22; Growing Ch. 5 & 13

Synonyms: _____

Antonyms: _____

Noun form of Thankful: _____

What person in the Bible illustrates this quality? Tell how: _____

_____

_____

Application: Write or draw how you can show this character trait.

Having a feeling or attitude of appreciation; grateful; expressing gratitude for a benefit received from another

THOUGHTFUL

Considerate; being careful not to offend; kind; wanting to do something extra for others; exercising care or thought

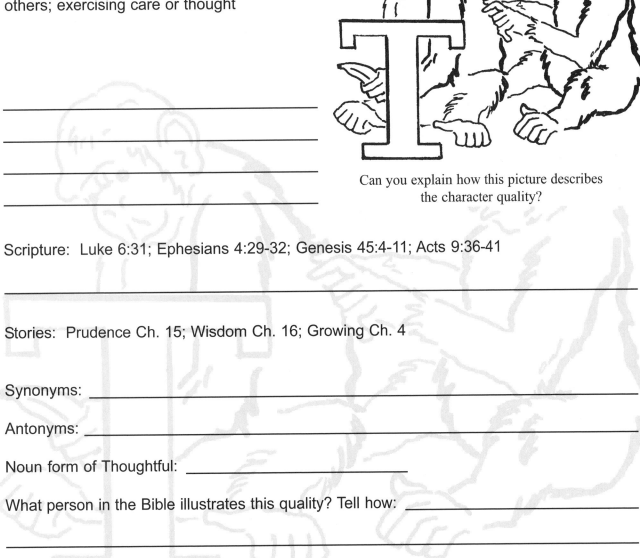

Can you explain how this picture describes the character quality?

_____
_____
_____
_____

Scripture: Luke 6:31; Ephesians 4:29-32; Genesis 45:4-11; Acts 9:36-41

_____

Stories: Prudence Ch. 15; Wisdom Ch. 16; Growing Ch. 4

Synonyms: _____

Antonyms: _____

Noun form of Thoughtful: _____

What person in the Bible illustrates this quality? Tell how: _____

_____

_____

Application: Write or draw how you can show this character trait.

Considerate;
being careful not to offend; kind; wanting to do something extra for others; exercising care or thought

45

TRUTHFUL

Telling the truth; honest; not deceptive

Can you explain how this picture describes
the character quality?

_____

_____

_____

_____

Scripture: Acts 4:36-5:11; Psalm 15:1-2; Ephesians 4:25, 6:13-14; John 14:6; Proverbs 12:22

_____

Stories: Prudence Ch. 4; School Days Ch. 21; Wisdom Ch. 10; Growing Ch. 10

Synonyms: _____

Antonyms: _____

Noun form of Truthful: _____

What person in the Bible illustrates this quality? Tell how: _____

_____

_____

Application: Write or draw how you can show this character trait.

Telling the truth; honest; not deceptive

UNSELFISH

Sharing with others fairly; not greedy or covetous; thinking of others; caring for others and not only yourself

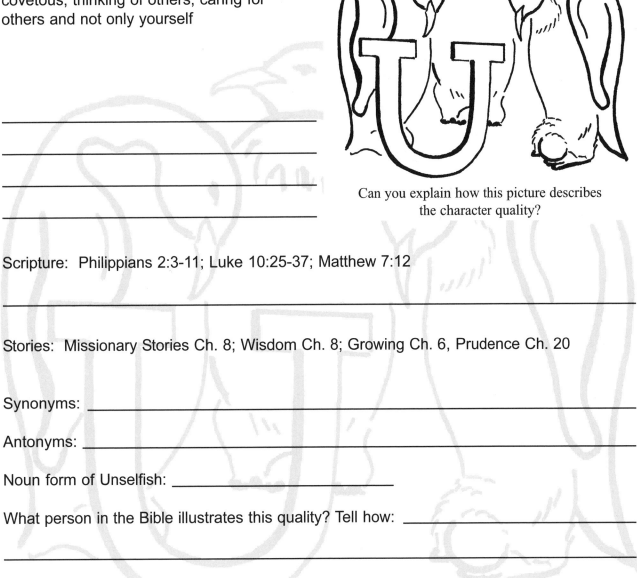

Can you explain how this picture describes the character quality?

_____
_____
_____
_____

Scripture: Philippians 2:3-11; Luke 10:25-37; Matthew 7:12

_____

Stories: Missionary Stories Ch. 8; Wisdom Ch. 8; Growing Ch. 6, Prudence Ch. 20

Synonyms: _____

Antonyms: _____

Noun form of Unselfish: _____

What person in the Bible illustrates this quality? Tell how: _____

_____

_____

Application: Write or draw how you can show this character trait.

VALIANT

Brave; courageously fulfilling a difficult position or duty; heroic

_____
_____
_____
_____

Can you explain how this picture describes the character quality?

Scripture: Joshua 1:7-9; Hebrews 11:24-27, 32-34; Numbers 13:26-33, 14:6-9; Ephesians 6:10-13

_____

Stories: Missionary Stories Ch. 4, 10, 14 & 16; School Days Ch. 1 & 23; Growing Ch. 2

Synonyms: _____

Antonyms: _____

Noun form of Valiant: _____

What person in the Bible illustrates this quality? Tell how: _____
_____
_____

Application: Write or draw how you can show this character trait.

Brave; courageously fulfilling a difficult position or duty; heroic

WISE

Skillful and proper use of one's abilities and resources; doing things the right way; ability to use knowledge in a beneficial way; ability to discern between good and evil

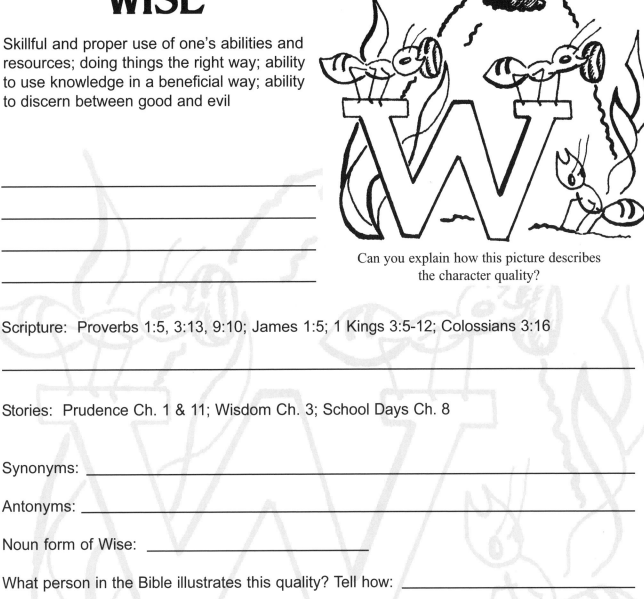

Can you explain how this picture describes the character quality?

_____
_____
_____
_____

Scripture: Proverbs 1:5, 3:13, 9:10; James 1:5; 1 Kings 3:5-12; Colossians 3:16

_____

Stories: Prudence Ch. 1 & 11; Wisdom Ch. 3; School Days Ch. 8

Synonyms: _____

Antonyms: _____

Noun form of Wise: _____

What person in the Bible illustrates this quality? Tell how: _____

_____

_____

Application: Write or draw how you can show this character trait.

Skillful and proper use of one's abilities and resources; doing things the right way; ability to use knowledge in a beneficial way; ability to discern between good and evil

49

EXEMPLARY

A good example or pattern to follow; worthy of imitation; a role model

Can you explain how this picture describes the character quality?

_____
_____
_____
_____

Scripture: Hebrews 11; 1 Timothy 4:12; John 13:12-15; 1 Peter 2:21-24; 2 Timothy 1:2-5

_____

Stories: Missionary Stories Introduction; Prudence Ch. 7 & 23; School Days Ch. 10

Synonyms: _____

Antonyms: _____

Noun form of Exemplary:_____

What person in the Bible illustrates this quality? Tell how: _____

_____

_____

Application: Write or draw how you can show this character trait.

A good example or pattern to follow; worthy of imitation; a role model

XENOPHILIC
(HOSPITABLE)

Graciously sharing one's home with others; making others feel welcome and comfortable in your home

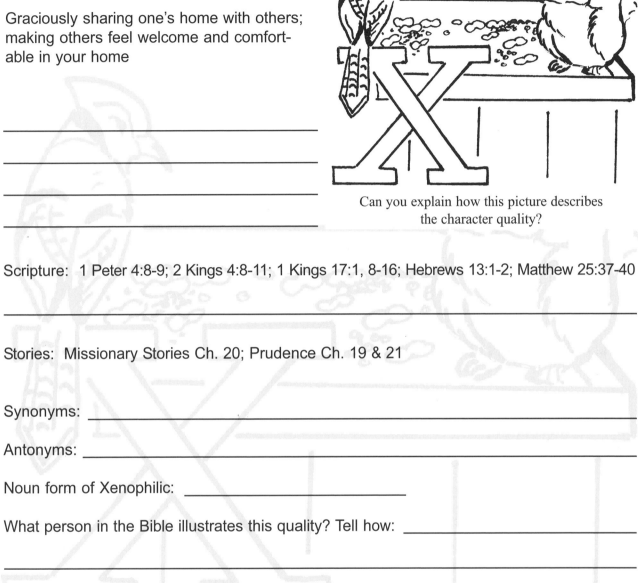

_____

_____

_____

_____

Can you explain how this picture describes the character quality?

Scripture: 1 Peter 4:8-9; 2 Kings 4:8-11; 1 Kings 17:1, 8-16; Hebrews 13:1-2; Matthew 25:37-40

_____

Stories: Missionary Stories Ch. 20; Prudence Ch. 19 & 21

Synonyms: _____

Antonyms: _____

Noun form of Xenophilic: _____

What person in the Bible illustrates this quality? Tell how: _____

_____

_____

Application: Write or draw how you can show this character trait.

YIELDING

Sacrificing one's will or rights to another; to comply; to give up; submitting

_____
_____
_____
_____

Can you explain how this picture describes
the character quality?

Scripture: Romans 6:11-13, 16-19, 12:10; Luke 15:11-24; Matthew 26:36-39; 2 Chronicles 30:7-8

_____

Stories: School Days Ch. 11; Storytime Ch. 7; Growing Ch. 22

Synonyms: _____

Antonyms: _____

Noun form of Yielding: _____

What person in the Bible illustrates this quality? Tell how: _____

_____

_____

Application: Write or draw how you can show this character trait.

Sacrificing one's will or rights to another; to comply; to give up; submitting

ZEALOUS

Being enthusiastic; dedicated and ambitious; not lazy or indifferent; whole-hearted

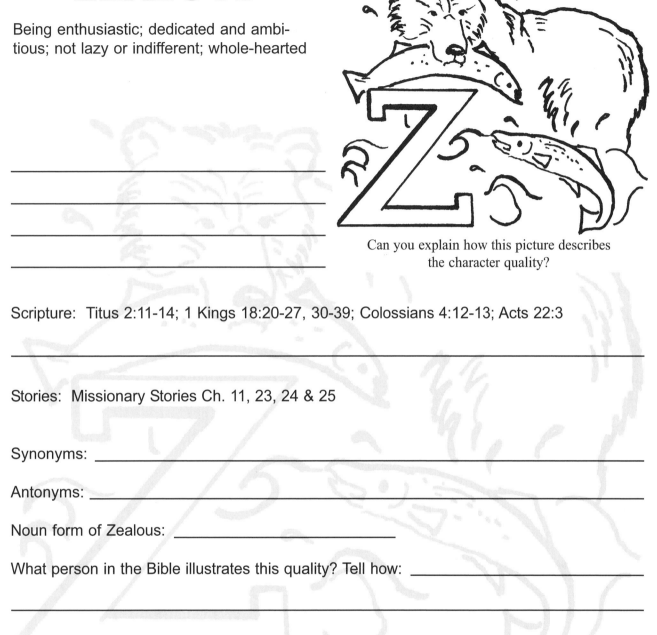

Can you explain how this picture describes the character quality?

_____

_____

_____

_____

Scripture: Titus 2:11-14; 1 Kings 18:20-27, 30-39; Colossians 4:12-13; Acts 22:3

_____

Stories: Missionary Stories Ch. 11, 23, 24 & 25

Synonyms: _____

Antonyms: _____

Noun form of Zealous: _____

What person in the Bible illustrates this quality? Tell how: _____

_____

_____

Application: Write or draw how you can show this character trait.

ALERT

Sure of; without doubt or hesitancy; having full belief; trusting

ATTENTIVE

Insightful; ability to accurately determine right from wrong; having keen understanding

BRAVE

Able to control oneself; well behaved and self-motivated; subjected to rules and regulations

CONFIDENT

Quick to detect; watchful; wide awake; guarding against surprise or danger

CONTENT

Courageous; fearless; doing what is right in spite of danger or hardships

DILIGENT

Satisfied; happily restful or peaceful; not covetous or greedy; having a mind at peace

DISCERNING

To listen or look at with interest; to pay attention; to closely follow; regarding with care

DISCIPLINED

Careful; putting forth earnest and honest effort; not lazy or slothful; constant in effort to accomplish what is undertaken

ENCOURAGING

Like or similar to God; righteous; living in obedience to God's commands, out of love for Him and reverence for His character and precepts

FAITHFUL

Patient and kind help or disposition; mild and peaceable behavior; soothing, not harsh

FORGIVING

Reliable; dependable; obedient; standing firm to a belief or practice; firmly adhering to duty; loyal

FRIENDLY

Giving good advice or council that is beneficial, uplifting or edifying; words or deeds that give courage to another; inspiring with hope and confidence

GENEROUS

Giving up personal revenge, spite or ill will against a person that has wronged you; not holding a grudge against; pardoning

GENTLE

That which is right, sound and beneficial; without significant fault or defect; virtuous; proper; favorable to happiness

GODLY

Socially kind and agreeable; expressing a feeling of openness and love towards another

GOOD

Granting or giving plenty; willingness to give ample or liberal amount

HELPFUL	Truthful; standing by the right even under pressure; giving fair value or measure; not cheating
HOLY	Full of joy; happy and thankful
HONEST	Without guilt or shame; free of wrong; blameless; pure
HUMBLE	Possessing and understanding a wide range of truth and facts; well informed
INNOCENT	Considerate and gracious; helpful; agreeable or benevolent in attitude and actions; looking out for the welfare of others often at the expense of self-comfort
JOYFUL	Ready to be of service or assistance; useful; willing to help
KIND	Without sin or fault, pure, undefiled, righteous, perfect; (God is holy in the absolute sense of the word. Man can be a partaker of God's holiness.)
KNOWLEDGEABLE	A quality of heart that is meek, quiet and gentle; not boastful, proud or showing off; not demanding

LOVING

Lowly in heart, humble, not boastful or proud; wanting to quietly do the right thing; submissive obedience; given to forbearance under injuries

MEEK

Graciously forbearing and forgiving; kindly withholding punishment due to an offender; compassionate

MERCIFUL

To be devoted to, kindly care for, admiring of; genuine love includes the qualities of self-sacrificing and commitment to another

NEAT

Following directions or commands; doing what one is supposed to do or not doing what is not allowed; submission to authority

OBEDIENT

Able to make relationships happy and harmonious; bringing unity; not causing strife or ill feelings; quiet and restful

PATIENT

Continuing on even though there are difficult obstacles; faithful; not giving up or turning back

PEACEABLE

Quietly waiting; not frustrated or hurried; contentedly waiting on God's timing; not overly demanding of others; not easily upset

PERSEVERING

Orderly; tidy; harmonious arrangement; well kept

PRUDENT

Reliable; trustworthy; fulfilling one's duties promptly and carefully; accountable

QUIET

Showing proper behavior and response toward others; treating others with dignity or kindness and esteem; using things in a careful way

RESOURCEFUL

Having a feeling or attitude of appreciation; grateful; expressing gratitude for a benefit received from another

RESPECTFUL

Insightful; good at avoiding danger or trouble; good judgment; cautious; circumspect; wise

RESPONSIBLE

Helping others, often at the expense of one's own interests; sensing what should be done by way of duty or need and doing it

SELF-CONTROLLED

Restful silence; absence of noise or commotion; still, peaceful

SERVING

Willing obedience; yielding one's will to the will of another; a humble person will have a submissive attitude

SUBMISSIVE

Able to keep one's appetites, desires and emotions in proper balance to what is wholesome and expedient; temperate; self-restraint

THANKFUL

Thrifty; good at making do with what you have at hand; creative

THOUGHTFUL	Sharing with others fairly; not greedy or covetous; thinking of others; caring for others and not only yourself
TRUTHFUL	Skillful and proper use of one's abilities and resources; doing things the right way; ability to use knowledge in a beneficial way; ability to discern between good and evil
UNSELFISH	Being enthusiastic; dedicated and ambitious; not lazy or indifferent; whole-hearted
VALIANT	A good example or pattern to follow; worthy of imitation; a role model
WISE	Considerate; being careful not to offend; kind; wanting to do something extra for others; exercising care or thought
EXEMPLARY	Sacrificing one's will or rights to another; to comply; to give up; submitting
XENOPHILIC	Telling the truth; honest; not deceptive
YIELDING	Graciously sharing one's home with others; making others feel welcome and comfortable in your home
ZEALOUS	Brave; courageously fulfilling a difficult position or duty; heroic

Answer Key

Can you explain how this picture describes the character quality?

Example for Alert:

A fox uses its ears, eyes and nose to help it to be alert to danger and to find food.

Noun forms of the character qualities

Alert — Alertness	Meek — Meekness
Attentive — Attentiveness	Merciful — Mercy
Brave — Bravery	Neat — Neatness
Confident — Confidence	Obedient — Obedience
Content — Contentment	Patient — Patience
Diligent — Diligence	Peaceable — Peace/Peacemaker
Discerning — Discernment	Persevering — Perseverance
Disciplined — Discipline	Prudent — Prudence
Encouraging — Encouragement	Quiet — Quietness
Faithful — Faithfulness	Resourceful — Resourcefulness
Forgiving — Forgiveness	Respectful — Respectfulness
Friendly — Friendliness	Responsible — Responsibility
Generous — Generosity	Self-controlled — Self-control
Gentle — Gentleness	Serving — Servant/Service
Godly — Godliness	Submissive — Submission
Good — Goodness	Thankful — Thankfulness
Helpful — Helpfulness	Thoughtful — Thoughtfulness
Holy — Holiness	Truthful — Truthfulness
Honest — Honesty	Unselfish — Unselfishness
Humble — Humility	Valiant — Valor
Innocent — Innocence	Wise — Wisdom
Joyful — Joyfulness	eXemplary — example
Kind — Kindness	Xenophile (Greek) — Xenophile (Greek)/Hospitality
Knowledgeable — Knowledge	Yielding — Yieldedness
Loving — Love/Lover	Zealous — Zeal